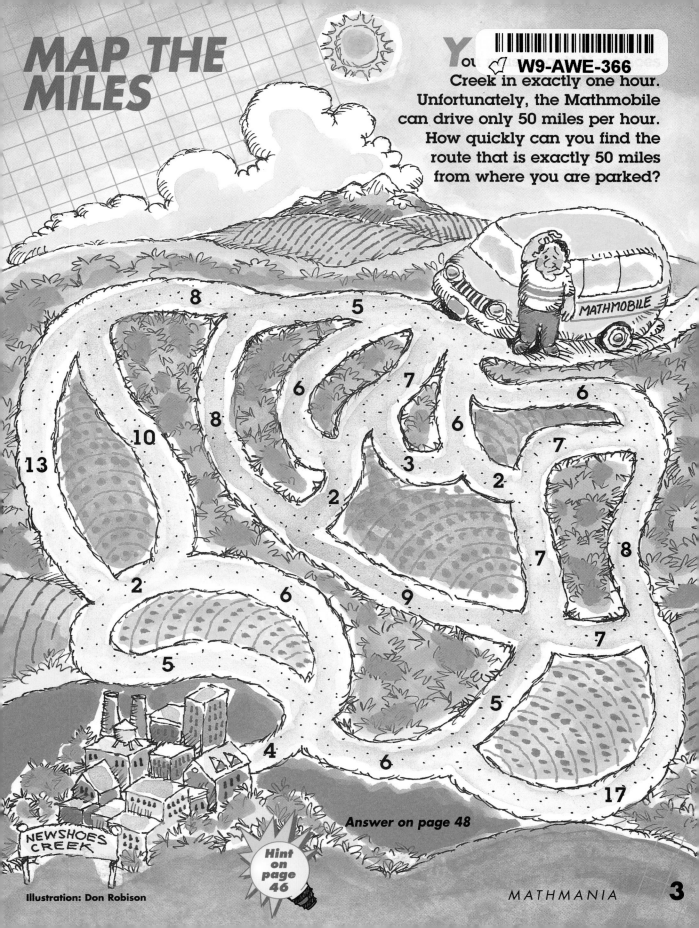

MAP THE MILES

You [must reach] ... Creek in exactly one hour. Unfortunately, the Mathmobile can drive only 50 miles per hour. How quickly can you find the route that is exactly 50 miles from where you are parked?

W9-AWE-366

8

5

6

7

6

8

10

7

3

6

2

7

13

2

9

7

2

6

8

5

7

5

4

6

17

Answer on page 48

Hint on page 46

NEWSHOES CREEK

Illustration: Don Robison

PLACE VALUES

You can put each famous landmark or geographical feature back on the proper continent by working some numbers.

South Pole
6 × 6 + 6 − 18

Victoria Falls
30 + 6 − 24 + 4

Mount Rushmore
100 ÷ 4 × 2

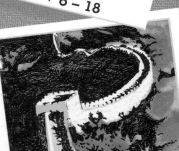

Great Wall of China
(3 + 2) × 8 − 10

Rio de Janeiro
(32 + 1) × 3

Eiffel Tower
5 × 5 × 2 − 5

45—Europe

50—North America

16—Africa

99—South America

Answer on page 48

24—Antarctica

Do the problem underneath each famous place. The answer for each should match the number on one of the continents listed.

To work these problems, go from left to right, doing each operation in order.

Taj Mahal
(66 − 6) ÷ 3 + 10

London Bridge
(5 + 5) × 5

Nile River
2 × 2 × 2 × 2

Big Ben
(40 ÷ 4) − 5 × 9

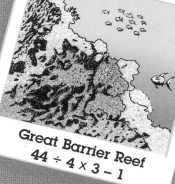

Great Barrier Reef
44 ÷ 4 × 3 − 1

Amazon River
11 × 3 × 3

30—Asia

Uluru (formerly Ayers Rock)
99 ÷ 3 − 1

Hint on page 46

32—Australia

Illustration: Jim Downer

BLACKOUT!

Black out the squares listed for each row. When you're done, the remaining letters will spell out the answer to our riddle.

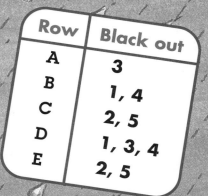

Row	Black out
A	3
B	1, 4
C	2, 5
D	1, 3, 4
E	2, 5

When can six people share one umbrella without getting wet?

	1	2	3	4	5
A	W	H	O	E	N
B	C	T	H	O	E
C	S	E	U	N	T
D	R	I	T	P	S
E	O	L	U	T	D

Answer on page 48

Illustration: Diana Zourelias

PARTY TIME

Chas and Charlotte were invited to a party at 7:00 p.m. on Saturday. Each arrived separately, though both were late. Use the clues to figure out what time each finally arrived.

Hint on page 46

PARTY HERE

Illustration: Doug Cushman

Each arrived within a half-hour of the starting time.

All three digits of Chas's arrival time are different.

The middle digit of Chas's arrival time is 5 less than the first digit.

The last two digits of Chas's arrival time are equal to the first digit.

Charlotte arrived 6 minutes before Chas.

Answer on page 48

WELL, AISLE B

BOX 2   Aisle ___

Last $\frac{1}{2}$ of TUBA
First $\frac{1}{2}$ of SEED
Last $\frac{1}{2}$ of FOOTBALL
First $\frac{3}{4}$ of GLOW
First $\frac{3}{4}$ of VEST

___ ___ ___ ___ ___ ___

BOX 1   Aisle ___

Last $\frac{3}{4}$ of WRAP
Last $\frac{1}{2}$ of SLID
Last $\frac{5}{6}$ of TRACER
3 × 5
First $\frac{1}{2}$ of SPIN
Last $\frac{3}{4}$ of NEED

___ ___ ___ ___ ___ ___ ___

___ ___ - ___ ___ ___ ___

BOX 3   Aisle ___

First $\frac{2}{3}$ of DOG
Last $\frac{4}{7}$ of TRACTOR
First $\frac{2}{5}$ of DOING
First $\frac{1}{2}$ of GOODNESS
Last $\frac{3}{4}$ of IDOL
Last $\frac{2}{5}$ of BELLS

___ ___ ___ ___ ___ ___

___ ___ - ___ ___ ___ ___

___ ___ ___ ___

what's inside each box?
Then check the chart on the
wall and write in the proper
aisle where each box belongs.

PRODUCT	AISLE
Books	A
Bicycles	B
Puzzles	C
Electronics	D
Games	E
Sports Equipment	F
Die-cast Cars	G
Dolls	H

BOX 4   Aisle___

Last $\frac{1}{2}$ of DOOR
First $\frac{4}{5}$ of ANGEL
First $\frac{1}{2}$ of CATSUP
First $\frac{1}{2}$ of JIGGLE
First $\frac{2}{3}$ of SAD
Last $\frac{1}{2}$ of MOWS

_ _ _ _ _ _   _ _ _ _

_ _ _ _ _ _

BOX 5   Aisle___

First $\frac{1}{2}$ of COMPLETE
Last $\frac{3}{4}$ of CUTE
Last $\frac{3}{5}$ of PORCH
Last $\frac{3}{5}$ of SLIPS

_ _ _ _ _ _ _ _ _

_ _ _ _ _

BOX 6   Aisle___

First $\frac{1}{2}$ of HANDSOME
Last $\frac{5}{8}$ of MARYLAND
Last $\frac{2}{5}$ of OMEGA
First $\frac{1}{3}$ of MENTAL

_ _ _ _ _ _ _ _

_ _ _ _

BOX 7   Aisle___

10 × 10
Last $\frac{3}{7}$ of FREEWAY
Last $\frac{5}{9}$ of DRUGSTORE
First $\frac{1}{2}$ of CYAN
First $\frac{3}{5}$ of CLEAN

_ _ _ _   _ _ _ _ _

_ _ _ _   _ _ _ _ _ _

BOX 8   Aisle___

First $\frac{1}{2}$ of THIS
First $\frac{2}{3}$ of UNDERWEAR
First $\frac{1}{2}$ of HEAP
Last $\frac{3}{7}$ of SHOVELS
First $\frac{3}{7}$ of RACCOON
Last $\frac{1}{2}$ of CHEESE
First $\frac{1}{4}$ of TIME

_ _ _ _ _ _ _ _ _ _ _

_ _ _ _ _ _ _ _ _

_ _ _ _ _ _ _ _ _

Illustration: Rick Geary

BAGEL BAKERS

The cooking class has been baking bagels. Can you tell how many bagels each person baked as well as how many bagels were baked altogether?

Andre baked half as many as Chuck.
Betty baked as many bagels as both Jane and Larry together.
Chuck baked twice as many as Larry.
Donna baked half as many as Glenn.
Glenn baked 10 more bagels than Betty.
Jane baked 4 more bagels than Andre.
Larry baked $3\frac{1}{2}$ dozen bagels.
Mary baked 7 more bagels than Donna.
Pablo baked half as many bagels as Sue.
Sue baked half as many bagels as Mary.

Hint on page 46

Illustration: John Nez

Answer on page 48

DOTS A LOT

Count by 4s to connect these dots and find a nice place to rest.

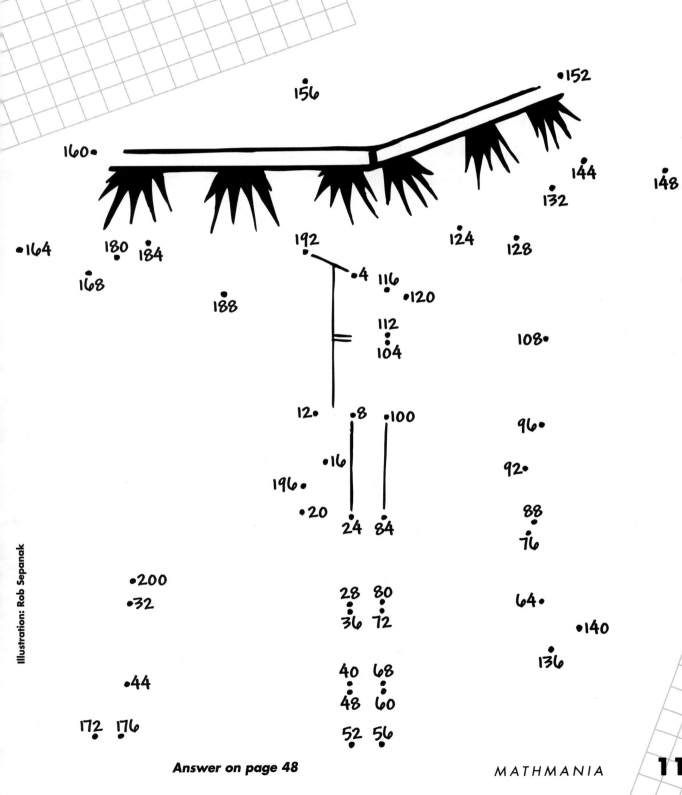

Illustration: Rob Sepanak

Answer on page 48

MATHMANIA **11**

CROSSNUMBER

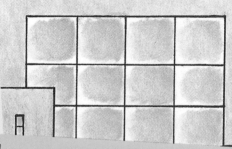

Answer each question as you would in a regular crossword, and then place the numbers into the grid, one number per box. Many of the clues relate to different games and sports.

ACROSS

1. 300 − 90
4. 300 + 300 + 15
7. Percentage equal to $\frac{1}{2}$
8. Number of pieces on the board at the start of a chess game
9. Height in feet of a regulation basketball hoop (100 − 90)
10. 75 + 25 + 3
12. Number of holes on a regulation golf course (2 × 9)
13. 10000 − 2880
15. Amount of money a player starts off with in Monopoly (500 × 3)
17. Number of leagues under the sea in a Jules Verne book (10 × 2000)
18. Last four countdown numbers
20. 1100 − 19
23. 3 × 10
24. Number of tiles in a standard game of Mah-Jongg (100 + 30 + 6)
26. Number of outs a pitcher records when pitching a perfect game
27. One dozen
28. Unlucky number, or a baker's dozen
29. Name of a dart game, or 240 + 261
30. Number of squares on the board in a game of Snakes & Ladders (10 × 10)

DOWN

1. 1250 + 1267
2. Number of tales of the Arabian Nights (15 Across − 499)
3. Number of white pieces in the game of Go (12 Across × 10)
5. Ten after one in the afternoon in military time (1200 + 110)
6. Number of feet in a mile
10. First palindromic number after 9999
11. 30000 + 1000 + 16
14. Baker Street address of Sherlock Holmes (1 Across + 11)
16. Number of miles in famous Indianapolis car race
18. 3300 + 15
19. Good eyesight
21. 4010 + 4200
22. 2000 − 270
25. Perfect bowling score

Hint on page 46

Answer on page 49

Illustration: Rick Geary

FAMOUS NAME

Illustration: Kit Wray

If you connect the dots in the order listed, you will find the name of the person described in this autobiography.

I was born in April 1743. I prepared the first draft of the Declaration of Independence. I served as a state governor, a member of the Continental Congress, the secretary of state for the entire nation, and the third President of the United States.

A B C D E F G H I J K L M N O P Q R

1
2
3
4
5
6

A1-C1	F1-G1	H1-I2	K1-L1	M1-N1	D2-E2	I2-J1	K2-L2
M2-N2	F3-G3	M3-N3	C4-D4	E4-F4	G4-H4	I4-J4	K4-L4
M4-N4	O4-P4	Q4-R6	C5-D5	E5-F5	G5-H5	I5-J5	K5-L5
K5-L6	M5-N5	A6-B6	C6-D6	I6-J6	M6-N6	O6-P6	R6-R4
B1-B3	D1-D3	E1-E3	F1-F3	G1-G3	H1-H3	J1-J3	K1-K3
L1-L3	M1-M2	N2-N3	B4-B6	C4-C6	E4-E6	G4-G6	I4-I6
K4-K6	L4-L5	M4-M5	O4-O6	P4-P6	Q4-Q6	A5-A6	N5-N6

Answer on page 49

STACKING STANLEY

Illustration: R. Michael Palan

BALANCING ACT

Bart is baffled about how to balance these scales. You can help him by matching one object to each scale so that the weight

1 **5 POUNDS**

2 **200 POUNDS**

3 **4 POUNDS**

4 **1/2 OUNCE**

5 **500 POUNDS**

6 **20 POUNDS**

7 **1 POUND**

is equal on both sides. You don't need to know the exact weights. Just guess which object is closest to each weight.

Hint on page 46

8   **7 OUNCES**

9   **2 OUNCES**

10   **2½ POUNDS**

A   BREAD

B

C

D

E   DISH DETERGENT

F

G

H   ICE CREAM

I

J   30

Illustration: Bill Colrus

WHAT'S NEXT?

AC	DF	GI	_____
1, 2, 3	3, 4, 7	5, 6, 11	_____
10,000	1,000	100	_____
A	AB	AC	_____
			_____
60 seconds	1 minute	60 minutes	_____
1:00	2:30	4:00	_____
			_____

MISSING NUMBERS

A number from 0 to 9 can go into one of the blanks below. Some numbers may seem to fit in more than one slot, but there is only one unique combination that will allow you to use all ten numbers.

Hint on page 46

$$13 \times \boxed{} = 1\boxed{}$$

$$\boxed{}1 \div \boxed{} = 3$$

$$4 \times \boxed{} = 1\boxed{}$$

$$2\boxed{} \times 2 = 5\boxed{}$$

$$\boxed{}1 \div \boxed{} = 9$$

Illustration: Beth Griffis Johnson

Answer on page 49

DELIVERY DILEMMA

This is Hy Headline's first day as a paper carrier for the *Daily Puzzle Post*. He has a list of subscriber addresses to follow. Unfortunately, the houses have no numbers, and the streets have no names posted.

Answer on page 49

ADDRESSES	SUBSCRIBER
288 Splat Street	yes
292 Splat Street	no
296 Splat Street	yes
300 Splat Street	yes
301 Splat Street	yes
304 Splat Street	no
305 Splat Street	yes
210 Squash Street	yes
214 Squash Street	yes
722 Oompa Street	yes
726 Oompa Street	no
730 Oompa Street	yes
820 Oompa Street	no

Still, Hy knows that the lowest house number on any street is to the south or west. Can you help him use the information on the list to figure out the street names, the addresses, and which houses get a paper?

Hint on page 46

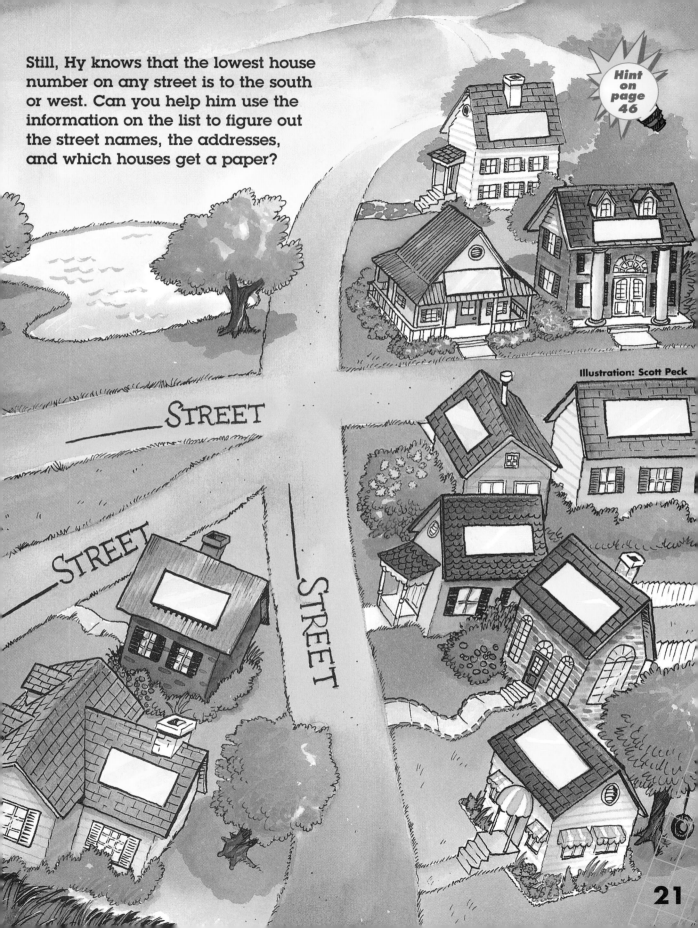

STREET

STREET

STREET

Illustration: Scott Peck

21

HANDFUL OF HORSES

Hillary wants to buy two horses of the same exact size at the auction. She knows that people measure horses in inches, centimeters, or hands. A hand is equal to 4 inches, and 2.54 centimeters equal 1 inch. Do you know which two horses Hillary will bid on?

STAR
3 YEARS OLD
12 HANDS

PENNY
4 YEARS OLD
162.56 CENTIMETERS

GINGER
2 YEARS OLD
52 INCHES

FLASH
5 YEARS OLD
46 INCHES

DAPPLE
5 YEARS OLD
142.24 CENTIMETERS

SALE

BLACKIE
2 YEARS OLD
14 HANDS

Answer on page 49

Illustration: Rick Geary

Hint on page 46

SANDY'S CANDIES

Ruth Babies $3.70   _____
Philip Cavity $5.25   _____
Etta Sweet $7.50   _____
Sue Crose $3.30   _____

Illustration: R. Michael Palan

Sandy is selling candy to help raise money for her choir. She wrote down how much each customer owes, but she forgot to write down the two items each person ordered. Since nobody ordered the same item, Sandy's sure she can figure out who gets what. Can you?

Answer on page 50

Chunks o' Chocolate
$4.00

Lots o' Licorice
$1.30

White Chocolate Melts
$3.00

Jilly's Jelly Beans
$2.50

Peppermint Puffs
$.80

Mint Cream Dreams
$2.25

Pecan Nutties
$3.50

Caramel Bites
$2.40

DIGIT DOES IT

The circus office of Goober's Big Top called Inspector Digit. An unhappy performer has left the show, and Goober is worried.

Goober gave the Inspector a note that was left behind. Can you help our man Digit crack this code and find the missing items?

$\overline{15}\ \overline{3}\ \overline{4}\ \overline{19}\quad \overline{5}\ \overline{14}\ \overline{14}\ \overline{8}\ \overline{3}\ \overline{19},$

$\overline{2}\ \overline{7}\ \overline{14}\ \overline{20}\quad \overline{7}\ \overline{19}\ \overline{22}\ \overline{13}\ \overline{10}\ \overline{5}\quad \overline{7}\ \overline{14},$

$\overline{8}\ \overline{11}\ \overline{7}\ \overline{7}\ \overline{3}\ \overline{19}\quad \overline{6}\ \overline{3}\quad \overline{11}\ \overline{20}\quad \overline{13}\ \overline{6}\quad \overline{13}\ \overline{10}$

$\overline{4}\quad \overline{16}\ \overline{4}\ \overline{6}\ ,\quad \overline{2}\ \overline{14}\quad \overline{13}\ \overline{6}\quad \overline{20}\ \overline{4}\ \overline{12}\ \overline{18}\ \overline{13}\ \overline{10}\ \overline{5}$

$\overline{6}\ ,\overline{22}\quad \overline{7}\ \overline{19}\ \overline{11}\ \overline{10}\ \overline{18}\quad \overline{4}\ \overline{10}\ \overline{15}\quad \overline{5}\ \overline{14}\ \overline{13}\ \overline{10}\ \overline{5}.$

$\overline{13}\ \overline{6}\quad \overline{7}\ \overline{13}\ \overline{19}\ \overline{3}\ \overline{15}\quad \overline{14}\ \overline{17}\quad \overline{21}\ \overline{14}\ \overline{19}\ \overline{18}\ \overline{13}\ \overline{10}\ \overline{5}$

$\overline{17}\ \overline{14}\ \overline{19}\quad \overline{20}\ \overline{3}\ \overline{4}\ \overline{10}\ \overline{11}\ \overline{7}\ \overline{2}\quad \overline{2}\ \overline{3}\ \overline{3}\quad \overline{13}\ \overline{17}$

$\overline{22}\ \overline{14}\ \overline{11}\quad \overline{12}\ \overline{4}\ \overline{10}\quad \overline{17}\ \overline{13}\ \overline{10}\ \overline{15}\quad \overline{7}\ \overline{9}\ \overline{3}$

$\overline{S}\ \overline{B}\quad \overline{20}\ \overline{3}\ \overline{4}\ \overline{10}\ \overline{11}\ \overline{7}\ \overline{2}\quad \overline{22}\ \overline{14}\ \overline{11}\quad \overline{14}\ \overline{21}\ \overline{3}\quad \overline{6}\ \overline{3}.$

$\overline{1}\ .\ \overline{3}\ .\quad \overline{17}\ \overline{11}\ \overline{10}\ \overline{7}$

Illustration: Joe Boddy

Hint on page 47

SCRAMBLED PICTURE

Copy these mixed-up rectangles onto the next page to unscramble the scene.

A-3   A-2   A-1   A-4

B-2   B-4   B-3   B-1

C-4   C-2   C-1   C-3

D-3   D-1   D-4   D-2

The letters and numbers
tell you where each rectangle
belongs. We've done the first
one, A-3, to start you off.

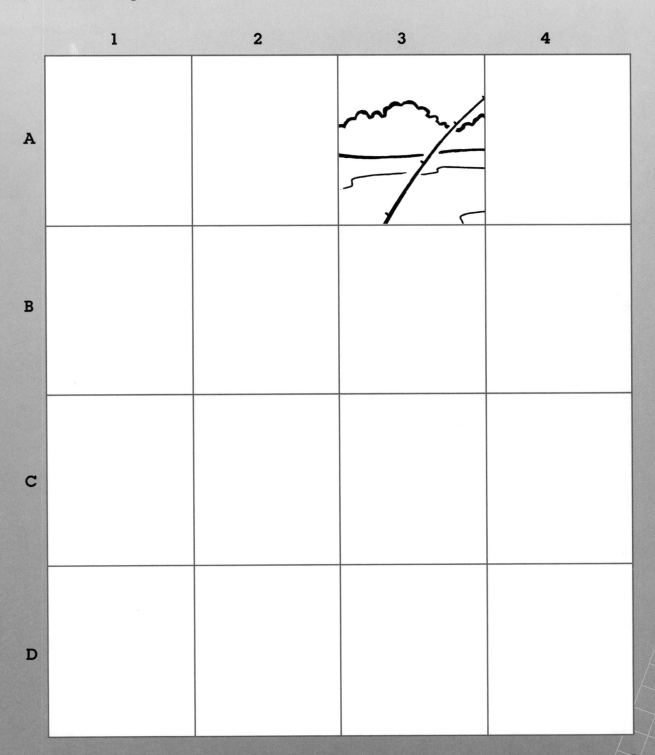

	1	2	3	4
A				
B				
C				
D				

Answer on page 50

FIFTY-FIFTY

Find the pairs of numbers that, when subtracted from each other, equal 50. Numbers may be above, below, across, or diagonally from each other. Every number will be part of one pair.

Answer on page 50

Hint on page 47

60	55	105	75	125	1005
1990	10	65	45	955	1015
2040	2100	2150	15	95	965
2000	1950	1960	1130	1180	1100
2500	1910	350	505	990	1150
2450	525	400	455	465	1040
475	325	375	415	950	1000

Illustration: Scott Peck

28

SIMONE SAYS

Simone wants to draw 4 straight lines in the square so that she will be left with 2 perfect squares and 4 triangles. Do you know how she can do it?

Hint on page 47

Illustration: R. Michael Palan

Answer on page 50

FIGURING THE FLOOR

The gymnasium is the largest room.

The school office is just to the right of the entrance and next to the art room.

The kitchen is next to the gym.

The math room is the first room on the left when you enter the building.

The library is half the size of the gym.

The English room is between the math and social studies rooms.

The girls' rest room is next to the music room.

The boys' rest room is the last room in the hall on the left.

The science lab is the smallest room to the right of the entrance.

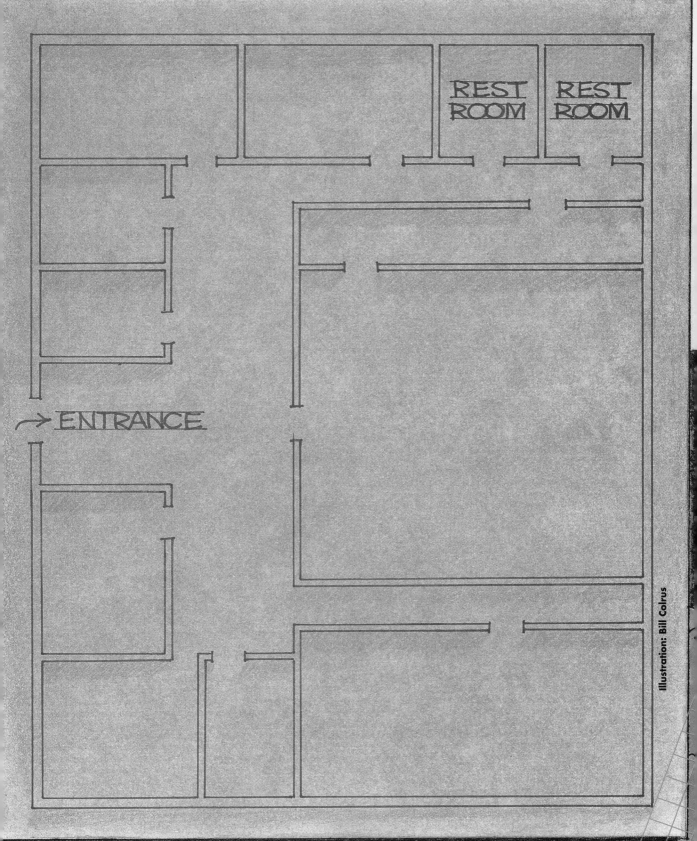

ENTRANCE

REST ROOM

REST ROOM

Illustration: Bill Colrus

LIBRARY LAUGHS

Dewey has some funny books in his library. To check one out, solve each problem. Then go to the shelves to find the volume with the number that matches each answer. Put the matching letter in the blank beside each answer. Read down the letters you've filled in to find the title and author of the book Dewey just finished reading.

Illustration: Scott Peck

Hint on page 47

Answer on page 50

$2 + 6 =$ _____
$3 \times 5 =$ _____
$28 \div 2 =$ _____
$8 - 3 =$ _____
$13 + 6 =$ _____
$4 \times 5 =$ _____
$26 - 3 =$ _____
$30 \div 2 =$ _____
$6 \times 3 =$ _____
$16 - 12 =$ _____
$17 + 2 =$ _____
$8 - 6 =$ _____
$5 \times 5 =$ _____
$24 \div 4 =$ _____
$3 \times 6 =$ _____
$44 - 43 =$ _____
$8 + 6 =$ _____
$33 \div 3 =$ _____
$3 \times 4 =$ _____
$14 - 9 =$ _____
$25 \div 5 =$ _____
$13 + 6 =$ _____
$2 \times 8 =$ _____
$19 - 14 =$ _____
$35 \div 7 =$ _____
$7 + 4 =$ _____
$3 \times 3 =$ _____
$9 + 5 =$ _____

FACE VALUE

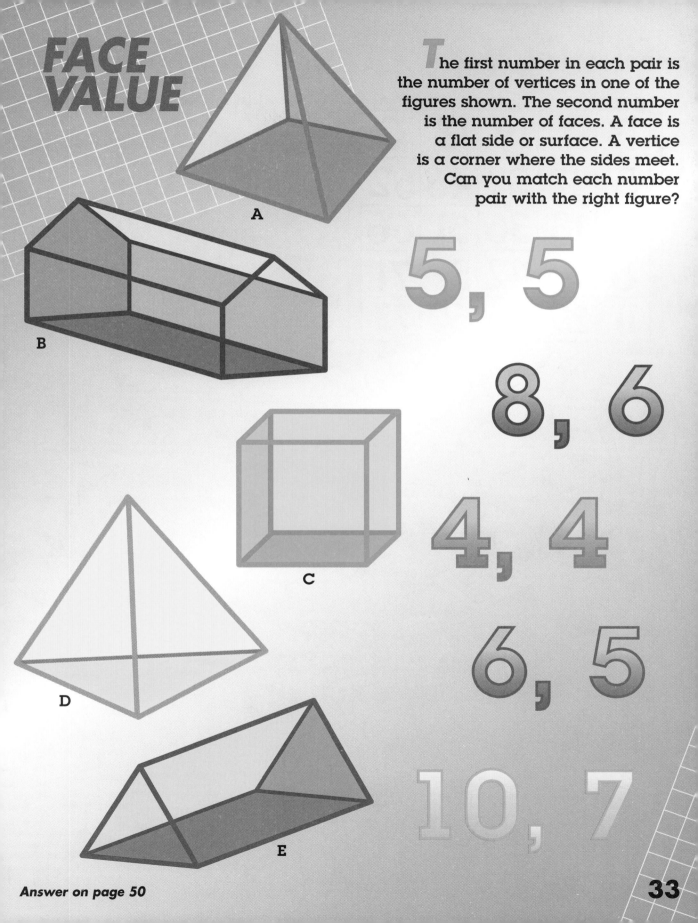

The first number in each pair is the number of vertices in one of the figures shown. The second number is the number of faces. A face is a flat side or surface. A vertex is a corner where the sides meet. Can you match each number pair with the right figure?

A

B

C

D

E

5, 5

8, 6

4, 4

6, 5

10, 7

Answer on page 50

BINGO!

B	I	N	G	O
5	17	32	46	62
7	18	36	51	66
8	20	42	57	71
11	29	44	60	73

out the numbers posted on the game board on the left-hand page. Can you tell who won?

Daisy

B	I	N	G	O
7	23	32	50	61
4	16	43	53	72
1	22	44	59	63
3	19	38	46	74
9	17	36	49	68

Flapper

B	I	N	G	O
4	22	37	46	69
9	28	32	54	61
12	17	44	50	71
5	23	39	48	74
14	24	41	53	75

Doogie

B	I	N	G	O
15	22	31	47	68
3	28	45	58	61
12	26	34	53	72
9	17	42	55	75
14	20	37	48	64

Chipper

B	I	N	G	O
15	26	34	47	61
7	19	35	51	73
3	29	42	60	68
10	16	32	49	62
2	20	38	57	70

Bruno

B	I	N	G	O
2	19	33	50	65
11	25	44	59	69
8	30	41	56	63
6	23	36	52	74
4	16	48	46	70

Cubbie

B	I	N	G	O
11	21	33	49	63
13	18	45	48	62
1	16	36	55	72
4	25	31	46	75
8	30	43	50	71

Kit

B	I	N	G	O
7	21	39	51	66
10	27	32	57	73
5	24	43	60	67
13	29	40	54	71
1	18	35	47	62

Reynard

B	I	N	G	O
2	16	31	51	73
11	23	34	47	62
15	24	44	54	70
8	29	41	49	75
6	19	38	59	66

Hint on page 47

Answer on page 50

MATHMAGIC

Remember these numbers:
13, 9, 5, 1.

Get 15 items of any kind—coins, candies, stones, anything. Put them on a table.

You and a friend take turns picking up these objects. You can take from one to three items at a time.

The object is to pick up all the items except the last one. Whoever gets stuck with the last one loses the game!

Can you figure out how to win every time? I'll reveal my answer on page 51.

Illustration: Marc Nadel

SAND ART

Can you draw this figure without crossing over or going back along any lines?

Illustration: Barbara Gray

Answer on page 51

37

HOCKEY HEROES

Who won the Oak County Hockey Conference? Use this season's headlines to fill in

BULLDOGS SHUT OUT SHARKS

STARS OUTSHINE FALCONS; BULLDOGS BEAT CHEETAHS

STARS SHOW FALCONS WHO'S BOSS

FALCONS FALL TO STARS

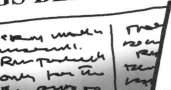

STARS FLY BY SHARKS OUTSKATE FALCONS

FALCONS LOSE TO CHEETAHS, BUT BEAT STARS

BULLDOGS TOP SHARKS AND FALCONS

BULLDOGS BEST FALCONS; FALCONS POUND CHEETAHS

STARS LOSE LAST GAME TO CHEETAHS

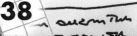

the win and loss columns. The trophy went to the team with the best record.

TEAM	WINS	LOSSES
Bulldogs		
Cheetahs		
Falcons		
Sharks		
Stars		

Illustration: Jerry Zimmerman

FALCONS BEAT SHARKS TWICE, BUT LOSE TO CHEETAHS

Answer on page 51

BULLDOGS TOPS OVER SHARKS AND CHEETAHS, BUT STARS OUTSCORE DOGS IN CLOSE GAME

SHARKS OVER CHEETAHS

SHARKS LOSE TO BULLDOGS AND CHEETAHS

SHARKS WIN BIG OVER STARS

BULLDOGS WIN IN OVERTIME AGAINST STARS

BULLDOGS TROUNCE STARS

CHEETAHS WIN; SHARKS LOSE

Hint on page 47

CHEETAHS WIN STREAK CONTINUES: BEAT SHARKS, STARS, AND BULLDOGS

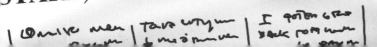

SCOOP UP SOME SLAW

Mary Jane has to make 20 pounds of coleslaw for her family picnic, so she needs to get 10 pounds of each ingredient. Which three cabbages and three bunches of carrots should she buy?

Illustration: R. Michael Palan

Hint on page 47

Answer on page 51

COLOR BY SHAPES

KEY

⚡ — Light Blue   ✕ — Brown
● — White   ★ — Yellow
▲ — Red   ■ — Gray

Illustration: John Puntar

Answer on page 51

PUZZLE OF A CENTURY

Good evening, and welcome to *This Was the 20th Century*. We will list three things that occurred in one of the ten different decades of the 1900s.

1900s
1910s
1920s
1930s
1940s
1950s
1960s
1970s
1980s
1990s

1. The *Titanic* sinks.
George V begins his reign as king of England.
Albert Einstein publishes his general theory of relativity.
(1000 × 2) − (30 × 3)

Hint on page 47

2. Jackie Robinson becomes the first African American to play baseball for a major league team, the Brooklyn Dodgers.
The Emmy Awards for television are first presented.
Velcro is invented.
(500 × 2) + 900 + (20 × 2)

3. Native Americans are given rights as U.S. citizens.
Charles Lindbergh makes his historic flight across the Atlantic Ocean.
Nellie Taylor Ross is the first woman elected governor in the U.S.
1900 + 5 + 5 + 5 + 5

It's up to you to match the events with a particular decade. If you need help, work the math problems.

4. The Wright brothers make their first flight.
   The first Nobel Peace Prizes are awarded.
   Women are allowed to compete in the modern Olympic Games for the first time.
   $(1000 \times 2) - (50 \times 2)$

5. Scientists clone a sheep.
   Major league soccer debuts in the United States.
   The *Pathfinder* and the *Global Surveyor* are launched to Mars.
   $2564 - 574$

6. The videocassette recorder is developed.
   Shirley Chisholm is the first African American woman elected to the U.S. Congress.
   The first human heart transplant is performed.
   $1326 + 603 + 31$

7. The Olympic Games are televised for the first time.
   Frozen foods are packaged by Clarence Birdseye.
   The first original comic book, *Famous Funnies*, is published. $(5000 \div 2) - 1000 + 415 + 15$

8. Sally Ride is the first American woman in space.
   Halley's Comet is seen for the second time this century.
   Ronald Reagan serves as 40th President of the United States.
   $1900 + 34 + 46$

9. The first rock-and-roll song makes the *Billboard* charts.
   Jonas Salk develops the polio vaccine.
   The first atomic-powered submarine is launched.
   $3900 \div 2$

10. The United States celebrates its bicentennial.
    The first food processor is invented in France.
    The first space station, *Skylab*, is put into orbit.
    $2100 - 100 - 25 - 5$

Answer on page 51

MATHMANIA

KEYSTONES

The entrance to this tunnel must be built in time for the new railroad to come through. Can you place the numbered stones in the outline so they will all fit? Once you've placed all the stones, can you guess which is the keystone, the one that holds the others in place?

Illustration: Jerry Zimmerman

Answer on page 51

IT FIGURES

Write the name of each geometric figure in the boxes beside it. When you are done, the letters in the yellow boxes will spell out the name of another figure.

Hint on page 47

HINTS AND BRIGHT IDEAS

*T*hese hints may help with some of the trickier puzzles.

MAP THE MILES (page 3)

The first two roads you should take are 7 miles long and 2 miles long. You must travel the complete length of any road.

PLACE VALUES (pages 4-5)

Be sure to do the problems from left to right, one step at a time. For example, the problem for Victoria Falls should be broken down like this: 30 + 6 = 36; 36 – 24 = 12; 12 + 4 = 16. 16 is the number for Africa.

PARTY TIME (page 7)

They arrived in the first half-hour, so they arrived sometime before 7:30 p.m.

BAGEL BAKERS (page 10)

Start with the number of bagels Larry baked. He baked 42 bagels. Write down each baker's name, then figure out his or her total.

CROSSNUMBER (pages 12-13)

A palindromic number is one that can be read the same backward as well as forward. All the digits in the number do not need to be the same.

BALANCING ACT (pages 16-17)

Start by finding the lightest weight on the scale. Now look for the lightest object. Then go to the heaviest and work that out.

MISSING NUMBERS (page 19)

13 times what number will give you a number in the teens?

DELIVERY DILEMMA (pages 20-21)

The list shows how many houses are on each street.

HANDFUL OF HORSES (page 22)

To work the conversion, divide the centimeter measurement by 2.54. You may want to use a calculator.

DIGIT DOES IT (pages 24-25)
This note is addressed *Dear Goober.* Use the code numbers from these words to help figure out the rest of the message.

FIFTY-FIFTY (page 28)
In the upper left corner, 60 and 10 make a pair. 60 − 10 = 50.

SIMONE SAYS (page 29)
One square is already there. The four lines Simone needs to draw will all come from the corners, or vertices. (See page 33 for more on vertices.)

LIBRARY LAUGHS (page 32)
Remember to consult the books to find the letter that matches each number.

BINGO! (pages 34-35)
To win at Bingo, you need to cross off five numbers in a row on your card as the numbers are called out. The five can go in any direction. To find which numbers to cross off on the cards, check the numbers posted on the board.

HOCKEY HEROES (pages 38-39)
Each team played a total of 12 games.

SCOOP UP SOME SLAW (page 40)
Mary Jane needs to buy 10 pounds of cabbage and 10 pounds of carrots. There are 16 ounces in a pound. Half a pound is 8 ounces.

PUZZLE OF A CENTURY (pages 42-43)
When working the problems, always do the operations in parentheses first. For instance, example 1 says (1000 × 2) − (30 × 3). The answer in the first set of parentheses is 2000, and the answer in the second set is 90. So now the problem reads 2000 − 90, which is 1910.

IT FIGURES (page 45)
The figures shown here include a sphere, a cube, a line, a cone, a pyramid, and a hexagon.

ANSWERS

BLACKOUT! (page 6)
When can six people share one umbrella without getting wet?
WHEN THE SUN IS OUT

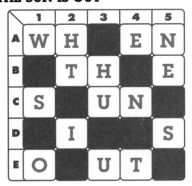

PARTY TIME (page 7)
Chas arrived at 7:25 p.m. Charlotte arrived at 7:19 p.m.

WELL, AISLE B (pages 8-9)

	PRODUCT	AISLE
BOX 1	RAPID RACER 15-SPEED	B
BOX 2	BASEBALL GLOVES	F
BOX 3	DOCTOR DO-GOOD DOLLS	H
BOX 4	ORANGE CAT JIGSAWS	C
BOX 5	COMPUTER CHIPS	D
BOX 6	HANDYLAND GAME	E
BOX 7	*100 WAYS TO RECYCLE*	A
BOX 8	THUNDER WHEELS RACE SET	G

BAGEL BAKERS (page 10)

Andre—42	Jane—46
Betty—88	Larry—42
Chuck—84	Mary—56
Donna—49	Pablo—14
Glenn—98	Sue—28

Total of all bagels: 547

DOTS A LOT (page 11)

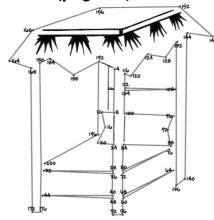

COVER
FISHING TODAY

MAP THE MILES (page 3)
Here is our answer. You may have found another.

PLACE VALUES (pages 4-5)

Mount Rushmore	50—North America
South Pole	24—Antarctica
Victoria Falls	16—Africa
Eiffel Tower	45—Europe
Great Wall of China	30—Asia
Rio de Janeiro	99—South America
Taj Mahal	30—Asia
London Bridge	50—North America
Nile River	16—Africa
Big Ben	45—Europe
Great Barrier Reef	32—Australia
Amazon River	99—South America
Uluru	32—Australia

CROSSNUMBER (pages 12-13)

FAMOUS NAME (page 14)

THOMAS JEFFERSON

STACKING STANLEY (page 15)

BALANCING ACT (pages 16-17)

1. F	3. E	5. B	7. A	9. D
2. J	4. G	6. I	8. C	10. H

WHAT'S NEXT? (page 18)

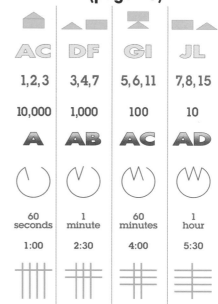

AC	DF	GI	JL
1, 2, 3	3, 4, 7	5, 6, 11	7, 8, 15
10,000	1,000	100	10
A	AB	AC	AD
60 seconds	1 minute	60 minutes	1 hour
1:00	2:30	4:00	5:30

MISSING NUMBERS (page 19)

$13 \times 1 = 13$
$21 \div 7 = 3$
$4 \times 4 = 16$
$25 \times 2 = 50$
$81 \div 9 = 9$

DELIVERY DILEMMA (pages 20-21)

HANDFUL OF HORSES (page 22)

Dapple: $142.24 \div 2.54 = 56$ inches
Flash: 46 inches
Star: $12 \times 4 = 48$ inches
Penny: $162.56 \div 2.54 = 64$ inches
Ginger: 52 inches
Blackie: $14 \times 4 = 56$ inches

Hillary will bid on Blackie and Dapple.

SANDY'S CANDIES (page 23)

Ruth Babies bought the Caramel Bites and the Lots o' Licorice ($2.40 + $1.30 = $3.70).

Philip Cavity bought the White Chocolate Melts and the Mint Cream Dreams ($3.00 + $2.25 = $5.25).

Etta Sweet bought the Pecan Nutties and the Chunks o' Chocolate ($3.50 + $4.00 = $7.50).

Sue Crose bought Jilly's Jelly Beans and the Peppermint Puffs ($2.50 + $.80 = $3.30).

DIGIT DOES IT (pages 24-25)

Dear Goober,

Stop trying to butter me up. I'm in a jam, so I'm packing my trunk and going. I'm tired of working for peanuts. See if you can find the 28 peanuts you owe me.

L. E. Funt

a-4	f-17	k-18	p-20	w-21
b-8	g-5	l-1	r-19	y-22
c-12	h-9	m-6	s-2	
d-15	i-13	n-10	t-7	
e-3	j-16	o-14	u-11	

SCRAMBLED PICTURE (pages 26-27)

FIFTY-FIFTY (page 28)

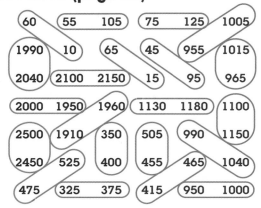

SIMONE SAYS (page 29)

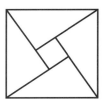

FIGURING THE FLOOR (pages 30-31)

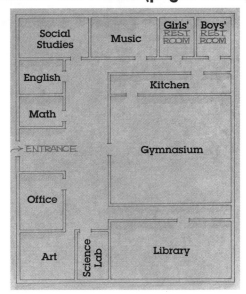

LIBRARY LAUGHS (page 32)

2 + 6 = 8	H	24 ÷ 4 = 6	F
3 × 5 = 15	O	3 × 6 = 18	R
28 ÷ 2 = 14	N	44 – 43 = 1	A
8 – 3 = 5	E	8 + 6 = 14	N
13 + 6 = 19	S	33 ÷ 3 = 11	K
4 × 5 = 20	T	3 × 4 = 12	L
26 – 3 = 23	W	14 – 9 = 5	E
30 ÷ 2 = 15	O	25 ÷ 5 = 5	E
6 × 3 = 18	R	13 + 6 = 19	S
16 – 12 = 4	D	2 × 8 = 16	P
17 + 2 = 19	S	19 – 14 = 5	E
8 – 6 = 2	B	35 ÷ 7 = 5	E
5 × 5 = 25	Y	7 + 4 = 11	K
		3 × 3 = 9	I
		9 + 5 = 14	N

HONEST WORDS by Frank Lee Speekin

FACE VALUE (page 33)

A—5, 5
B—10, 7
C—8, 6
D—4, 4
E—6, 5

BINGO! (pages 34-35)

Cubbie won.